Foreword

'My First Riddle' was a competition specifically designed for Key Stage 1 children. The simple, fun form of the riddle gives even the youngest and least confident writers the chance to become interested in poetry by giving them a framework within which to shape their ideas. As well as this it also allows older children to let their creativity flow as much as possible, encouraging the use of simile and descriptive language.

Given the young age of the entrants, we have tried to include as many poems as possible. We believe that seeing their work in print will inspire a love of reading and writing and give these young poets the confidence to develop their skills in the future.

Our defining aim at Young Writers is to foster the talent of the next generation of authors. We are proud to present this latest collection of anthologies and hope you agree that they are an excellent showcase of young writing talent.

Contents

The Poems

She Is My Mum

She is as helpful as a teacher.
She is as cute as a rose.
She is as funny as a clown.
She is as pretty as a princess.
She is my mum, Eileen.

Alana Mcnab (7)

My Mystery Guest

He is as smart as Archimedes.
He is as old as Elizabeth I
He is as talented as a musician who plays two instruments.
He is as famous as a film star.
He is as musical as a band.
He is as confident as a brilliant actor.
He is as cheerful as a happy person.
He is as fabulous as a crane
He was once caught up in a minor riot.
He is as nice as my friend, Ryan.
He is William Shakespeare.

Daniel McIlroy (8)
Ashgrove Primary School, Newtownabbey

Robinho

He is as fast as a roller coaster.
He is as rich as a president.
He is kinder than everyone.
He is as tall as a table.
He is as cool as a town cat.
He is as dark as the night sky.
He has more fans than ever.
He is as skinny as a leaf.
He is as confident as ever.
He is as good as gold.
He has more energy than a jet.
He is as talented as Miley Cyrus.
He is Robinho.

Ben McKenna (7)
Ashgrove Primary School, Newtownabbey

Kesha

She is as beautiful as a tulip.
She is as fast as rollerboots.
She is as tall as a giraffe.
She is as kind as my mum.
She is as bright as a lantern.
She is as funny as a clown.
She is as talented as an acrobat.
She is as sweet as candyfloss.
She is as cheeky as a monkey.
She is as cool as ice cream.
She is a brilliant singer.
She is as elegant as a petal.
She is as light as a cloud.
She is Kesha.

Lauren Hetherington (8)
Ashgrove Primary School, Newtownabbey

My Dad

He is as tall as a giant
He is as funny as a clown
He is as smart as a scientist
He is as kind as God
He is as fun as a waterslide
He is as bright as the sun
He is as cool as a cat
He is better than Steven Gerrard
He is as fast as a cheetah
He is as nice as a smiley face
He is my dad.

Rees Worthington (7)
Ashgrove Primary School, Newtownabbey

My Brother, Leon

He is as cheeky as a monkey
He is as happy as a flower
He is as bright as the sun
He is as medium tall as a medium dragon
He is as confident as a singer
He is as ugly as a dog
He is as cool as a footballer
He is as sweet as a Coca-Cola sweet
He laughs like a train
He is as fat as an elephant
He is my wee brother, Leon.

Wan-Min Zue (7)
Ashgrove Primary School, Newtownabbey

ABBA

They are as tall as the sun
They are as thin as a leaf
They are as confident as bees
They are as hot as fire
They are as musical as a guitar
They are as kind as a kitten
They are as famous as gold
They are as fabulous as butterflies
They are as smart as cats
They are as bright as the sun.

They are the group ABBA.

Philip Moore (7)
Ashgrove Primary School, Newtownabbey

Lazy Linda

She is as messy as my dad
She is as tired as my mum
She is as lazy as my guinea pig
She is as smelly as a pig
She is as crazy as an elephant
She is Lazy Linda.

Rachael McAulay (6)
Blacklands Primary School, Kilwinning

Horrid Henry

He is as smelly as socks.
He is as horrid as Moody Margaret.
He is a cool dude.
He is as weird as a mad inventor.
He is as cheeky as a monkey.
He is *Horrid Henry!*

Bella Stewart (7)
Blacklands Primary School, Kilwinning

Clever Clare

She is as clever as a teacher.
She is as tall as a lamp post.
She has hair like chocolate.
She is as quiet as a mouse.
She is as lovely as a peach.
She is as fast as a car.
She is Clever Clare.

Siana Dorrens (7)
Blacklands Primary School, Kilwinning

Greedy Graham

He is as tall as a giraffe.
He is as hairy as a monkey.
He is as disgusting as slime.
He is as greedy as a gorilla.
He is Greedy Graham.

Ben Irvine (6)
Blacklands Primary School, Kilwinning

Moody Margaret

She is as moody as a lion.
She is as bossy as my dad.
She's the best neighbour.
She's as skinny as a mouse tail.
She is as messy as my room.
She is as nasty as a monster.
She is Moody Margaret.

Joni Faddes (7)
Blacklands Primary School, Kilwinning

Horrid Henry

He is as horrid as a donkey.
He is as gross as gloop.
He is as disgusting as muck.
He is as cheeky as a monkey.
He is as nasty as a chimpanzee.
He is as smelly as a rotten egg.
He is Horrid Henry.

Evan Quinn (7)
Blacklands Primary School, Kilwinning

Horrid Henry

He is as cheeky as a monkey.
He's as small as an ant.
He is as noisy as an elephant.
He is Horrid Henry.

Kris Grimes (7)
Blacklands Primary School, Kilwinning

Lazy Linda

She is as lazy my mum.
She is as messy as my dad.
She is as fat as an elephant.
She is as long as a giraffe.
She is as grumpy as a dwarf.
She is as tired as a lion.
She is Lazy Linda.

Aimee McLaughlan (7)
Blacklands Primary School, Kilwinning

Tough Toby

He is as strong as the Loch Ness monster.
He is as chubby as an elephant.
He is as hairy as a chimpanzee.
He is as bossy as Mum.
He is as silly as a clown.
He is Tough Toby.

Ryan Morris (7)
Blacklands Primary School, Kilwinning

Moody Margaret

She is as moody as a teacher.
She is as bossy as a mum.
She is as lazy as a lion.
She is as clever as a referee.
She is as horrid as Horrid Henry.
She is Moody Margaret.

Brodie Tudhope (6)
Blacklands Primary School, Kilwinning

Horrid Henry

He is as nasty as a monkey.
He is as horrid as a bat.
He is as disgusting as gloop.
He is as smelly as a frog.
He is as fast as a cheetah.
He is Horrid Henry.

Jamie-Lee Hawthorne (6)
Blacklands Primary School, Kilwinning

Perfect Peter

He is as perfect as your mum.
He is as small as a frog.
He loves his mum like a love heart.
He loves school like a lovely person.
He is as slow as a turtle.
He is Perfect Peter.

Jemma Watt (7)
Blacklands Primary School, Kilwinning

Dizzy David

He's as dizzy as a spinning top
He's as skinny as a snake
He is as fast as Sonic
He is as silly as a clown
He's as good as gold
He is Dizzy David.

Daniel Sweeney (7)
Blacklands Primary School, Kilwinning

Moody Margaret

She is as moody as a bull.
She is as bossy as a pirate.
She is as tall as a giraffe.
She is as long as a snake.
She has a long neck like an ostrich.
She is Moody Margaret.

Beth Brannigan (7)
Blacklands Primary School, Kilwinning

Lazy Linda

She is as fat as an elephant
She is as grumpy as my gran
She is as messy as my toybox
She is as quiet as a whisper
She is Lazy Linda.

Kira McLaughlan (6)
Blacklands Primary School, Kilwinning

My House

It has a toilet.
It has a roof.
It has a garden.
It has windows.

Jaydon Mullen (4)
Blacklands Primary School, Kilwinning

My House

It has a TV
It has a toilet
It has a garage
It has a chimney.

Matthew McColgan (5)
Blacklands Primary School, Kilwinning

My House

It has a chimney.
It has a TV.
It has a garage.
It has windows.

Kian Lynch (5)
Blacklands Primary School, Kilwinning

The Gingerbread Man

He can run fast.
He is quick.
He's as nice as a daffodil.
He is the Gingerbread Man.

Saul Todd (6)
Blacklands Primary School, Kilwinning

He Is

He is kind like a mum.
He is real like a boy.
He is a cool boy.
He is wooden like a log.
He is Pinocchio.

Kayla Murphy (6)
Blacklands Primary School, Kilwinning

He Is

He is fast like a frog.
He is baked.
He is nice.
He is nice like a monkey.
He is the Gingerbread Man.

Liam McMaster (6)
Blacklands Primary School, Kilwinning

The Gingerbread Man

He is kind.
He is fast.
He is yummy.
He is baked.
He is the Gingerbread Man.

Connor Steven (7)
Blacklands Primary School, Kilwinning

Untitled

He is baked out of ginger.
He got eaten up.
He is fast like a missile.
He is as cool as a dragon.
He is the Gingerbread Man.

Ross Steel (6)
Blacklands Primary School, Kilwinning

Untitled

He is baked.
He is tasty.
He is fast like a missile.
He is nice like a butterfly.
He is the Gingerbread Man.

Lauchlin Ness (5)
Blacklands Primary School, Kilwinning

Rude Ralph

He is as rude as a boy.
He is as cool as a chipmunk.
He is as nasty as a bully.
He is as tall as a giraffe.
He is as fast as a car.
He is as loud as a barking dog.
He is Rude Ralph.

Elle Edmunds (7)
Blacklands Primary School, Kilwinning

The Gingerbread Man

He is kind.
He is fast.
He is baked.
He is the Gingerbread Man.

Adam Marno (6)
Blacklands Primary School, Kilwinning

Granny's Dog

She is as big as a horse
She eats as much as a pig
She is as fat as a bin
She poos as much as a hamster
She is Sal, my granny's dog.

Tathan Pritchard (5)
Bronllys Primary School, Bronllys

LuKey

Big as a giant
He runs in a field
He is as tidy as a chicken
He is as sick as a dog
He is Lukey, my horse.

Tia-Mai Graham (5)
Bronllys Primary School, Bronllys

Max The Hedgehog

He is as brown as the dirt.
He is as cute as a chocolate button.
He is as spiky as a bush.
He is as smart as a teacher.
He is as small as an ant.
He is Max the hedgehog.

Katie Black (6)
Broomlands Primary School, Broomlands

Max The Hedgehog

He is as cute as a kitten.
He is as lazy as a turtle.
He is as tiny as a pup.
He is sweet and sour.
He is as hungry as a gorilla.
He is as slow as a broken leg.
He is as nice as fluff.
He is as clever as a human.
He is as tickly as 100 spikes.
He is Max the hedgehog.

Cal McPherson (7)
Broomlands Primary School, Broomlands

Max The Hedgehog

He is as cheeky as a rabbit.
He is as spiky as a cactus.
He is as brown as dirt.
He is as beautiful as the sun.
He is Max the hedgehog.

Luke Nelson (6)
Broomlands Primary School, Broomlands

The Hodgeheg

He is as cute as a bunny.
He is as funny as a clown.
He is as cheeky as my wee brother.
He is as soft as a teddy bear.
He is as prickly as a cactus.
He is as beautiful as a flower.
He is as cool as a freezer.
He is as cosy as a bed.
He is Max the hodgeheg.

Lara Stewart (7)
Broomlands Primary School, Broomlands

The Hedgehog

He is as sweet as a lolly.
He is as cheeky as a monkey.
He is as soft as a teddy bear.
He is as small as an apple.
He is as cute as a monkey.
He is as smart as a teacher.
He is as prickly as a jaggy nettle.
He is as funny as a clown.
He is as brown as my eyes.
He is Max the hedgehog.

Natalie Mitchell (8)
Broomlands Primary School, Broomlands

The Hedgehog

He is as nice as a rabbit
He is as cheeky as a monkey
He is as smart as a lion
He is as cute as a dog
He is as jaggy as a nettle
He is as round as a football
He is as small as a snail
He is as slow as a slug
He is as big as a giant.

He is Max the hedgehog.

Aiden Richardson (8)
Broomlands Primary School, Broomlands

The Hedgehog

He is as jaggy as a thorn.
He is as cuddly as a teddy.
He is as cheeky as a monkey.
He is as cute as a guinea pig.
He is as small as a snail.
He is as round as a ball.
He is as smart as a teacher.
He is as adventurous as a human.
He is Max the hedgehog.

Abbie Cobley (8)
Broomlands Primary School, Broomlands

Who Am I?

I am blonde like the sun.
I have hair like a scarf.
I am pretty.
I am tall like a tree.
Who am I?

Shauna Osborne (6)
Bryn Celyn Primary School, Cardiff

Who Am I?

I am fast like a cheetah
I am stylish like a hairdresser
I am a footballer
I play for Liverpool
I am a striker
I am on TV
I am young
Who am I?

McKenzie Sell (6)
Bryn Celyn Primary School, Cardiff

Who Am I?

I am cuddly
I am playful
I am kind
I am pretty
Who am I?

Nicole Pritchard (6)
Bryn Celyn Primary School, Cardiff

Who Am I?

I have black hair like a cat.
I am a singer.
I am tall like a giraffe.
I can moonwalk.
Who am I?

Kyle Kelly (6)
Bryn Celyn Primary School, Cardiff

Who Am I?

I am a judge
I have black hair like a gorilla
I have a grey T-shirt
I am tall like a giraffe
I am nasty like a devil
I live in America
Who am I?

Aidan McCarthy (7)
Bryn Celyn Primary School, Cardiff

Who Am I?

I am a singer
I am as pretty as a butterfly
I am popular
I am stylish
I am as funny as a clown
Who am I?

Kirsten Hull (7)
Bryn Celyn Primary School, Cardiff

Who Am I?

I am scary
I am slimy
I have patterns
Who am I?

Naomi Pritchard (6)
Bryn Celyn Primary School, Cardiff

Who Am I?

I am as fast as you
I have a laugh
I have a lot of shoes
Who am I?

Katie Thomas (6)
Bryn Celyn Primary School, Cardiff

My Sister

She is as cute as a cat.
She steals my money like a thief
And hides it like a hedgehog.
She plays like a puppy
And is as cuddly as a teddy bear.

Erin Mary Winkelmann (6)
Bun-sgoil Shléite, Isle of Skye

A Fish

I don't bite
If I am not scared
If a shark sees me I will swim.
I swim fast.
I swim slow.

David McConnell (6)
Cleland Primary School, Cleland

A Jellyfish

I am as soft as sand.
I look like a ghost but move about in the sea.
I have stripes that hang from my body.
I sting other animals.
I look like half of a circle.
What am I?

I am a jellyfish.

Sean Muir (6)
Cleland Primary School, Cleland

A Crab

I am as orange as the sand.
I am as hard as a rock.
I can nip other creatures.
I move side to side.
You can find me in the sand.
What am I?

I am a crab.

Robbie Martin (7)
Cleland Primary School, Cleland

A Swordfish

I am like a sword.
I am pointy.
I am as hard as a rock.
I am big and fearless.
I am scary.
I have big eyes.
What am I?

I am a swordfish.

Adam Connor (5)
Cleland Primary School, Cleland

A Shark

I look like a really big fish.
I have very big teeth.
I eat big fish like a flat fish.
If you go close to me I might eat you.
I have got sharp fins.
I like going hunting for fish to eat.
I can swim fast.
What am I?

I am a shark.

Sophie Hyslop (6)
Cleland Primary School, Cleland

A Crab

I am as nippy as a sword
I can walk side to side.
I can pinch.
I am scary.
I am hard.
What am I?

I am a crab.

Zach O'Donnell (6)
Cleland Primary School, Cleland

A Jellyfish

I can sting.
I can grab things.
I am slimy.
I live under the water.
I float in the water.
What am I?

I am a jellyfish.

Kyle Savage (6)
Cleland Primary School, Cleland

A Swordfish

I am as scary as a shark.
I can kill.
You better not come near me
Or you will be my dinner.
I can put my nose in you.
What am I?

I am a swordfish.

Beth Ballantyne (6)
Cleland Primary School, Cleland

What Am I?

You will see me at the zoo.
I am very big and heavy.
I walk very slowly.
I have a long trunk.
What am I?

I am an elephant.

Evan Scott (7)
Cleland Primary School, Cleland

What Am I?

I have black spots.
I have razor-sharp teeth.
I like to run fast.
I am a warm-blooded animal.
I eat meat.
I live in hot places.
I like to hunt.
I like to swim in rivers.
Watch out you could be my dinner
If you're not careful!
What am I?

I am a cheetah.

Rhianna Thompson (8)
Cleland Primary School, Cleland

What Am I?

I am a wild animal.
I like to eat other animals.
I am a meateater.
I look like a dog.
I have sharp teeth.
I am not scared of other small animals.
I have a fluffy tail.
I have ginger skin the colour of gold.
I am a warm-blooded animal.
What am I?

I am a fox.

Abbie Kirk (7)
Cleland Primary School, Cleland

What Am I?

You will find me in the safari.
I am the colour of the clouds and I am black.
I can run fast.
I eat green stuff and people paint the road
To look like me.
I look like a horse but I'm not.
What am I?

I am a zebra.

Alyssa Louise Clifford (7)
Cleland Primary School, Cleland

Miss Dodd

She is as pretty as a flower
She is as happy as a butterfly
She is as clever as a monkey
She is as nice as chocolate
She is Miss Dodd.

**Amelia Ellis (5), Rebecca Thomas, Ben Price,
Ethan Davis (6), Lowri Watts & Dafydd Walsh (7)**
Coed-y-Lan Primary School, Graigwen

My Brother

He is as naughty as a monkey,
He is as silly as a clown,
He is as nice as a butterfly,
He is as good as a dog,
He is my brother, Charlie.

James Olding (6)
Coed-y-Lan Primary School, Graigwen

My Dog

He is as funny as a clown,
He really likes biscuits,
He is as daft as a monkey,
He is as hairy as a gorilla,
He is Tilly, my dog.

Kate Baynham (7)
Coed-y-Lan Primary School, Graigwen

My Dog

He is as funny as a clown,
He is as daft as a brush,
He is as naughty as a monkey,
He is as greedy as a pig,
He is Kingsley, my dog.

Maisie Jones (6)
Coed-y-Lan Primary School, Graigwen

My Mum

She is as pretty as a flower,
She cooks better than a chef,
She is as funny as a clown,
She is as helpful as my dad,
She is as kind as a butterfly,
She is my mum.

Samuel John (6)
Coed-y-Lan Primary School, Graigwen

Untitled

She is as soft as her brother
She is as cute as a flower
She is as nice as a person
She looks like a chocolate bar
She is as caring as a butterfly
She is as furry as a tiger
She is as strong as a lion
She is my pet rabbit
She is a friend.

Hannah Okon (6)
Coed-y-Lan Primary School, Graigwen

My Brother

He is as funny as a clown,
He is as fast as his dad,
He is as cheeky as a monkey,
He is as hungry as a caterpillar,
He is Ethan, my brother.

Ella Furmage (6)
Coed-y-Lan Primary School, Graigwen

My Brother

He is as funny as a flower,
He is as fast as lightning,
He is as nice as a cherry,
He is as cute as a rabbit,
He is my brother, Ryan.

Gemma Lauren Jones (6)
Coed-y-Lan Primary School, Graigwen

My Sister

She is as pretty as a rose,
She cooks better than a chef,
She is as funny as a monkey,
She is as fast as roller skates,
She is as special as a diamond,
She is my sister, Daniella.

Isabel Bedgood (6)
Coed-y-Lan Primary School, Graigwen

My Baby Brother

He is as naughty as a fox,
He pretends to be a monster,
He likes to watch 'In the Night Garden',
He is my baby brother, Tom.

Ben Dackins (5)
Coed-y-Lan Primary School, Graigwen

Imogen

She is as fast as the wind,
She is as cheeky as a monkey,
She is as funny as a clown,
She is as sweet as a berry,
She is my sister, Imogen.

Ella Tanner (6)
Coed-y-Lan Primary School, Graigwen

My Cat, Maisey

She is as pretty as a butterfly,
She is as nice as a sweet,
She is my cat called Maisey.

Emma Jameson (5)
Coed-y-Lan Primary School, Graigwen

My Rabbit

He can bounce like a kangaroo,
He is as fluffy as an owl,
He is as cute as a butterfly,
He likes to eat bananas,
He is Michael, my rabbit.

Theo Farrell (6)
Coed-y-Lan Primary School, Graigwen

About My Mum

She's as cool as a Slush Puppie.
She's as cute as a cupcake.
She as much fun as a fairground.
She's as tasty as chocolate.
She's the best mum in the world.

Alex Meneely (6)
Howard Primary School, Moygashel

My Sister

She jumps so high she can touch the moon.
She is as pink as strawberry ice cream.
She talks like a chatterbox.
She is as silly as a clown.
She plays football like an elephant.
She is as beautiful as summer.
She is as loud as thunder.
She is Emma, my sister.

Adam Curran (7)
Howard Primary School, Moygashel

My Sister

She is as pretty as a flower,
She's as cuddly as a bear,
She's as tall as a giraffe,
She's as clever as an owl,
She's as cheeky as a monkey,
She's as tidy as a squirrel,
She is my sister.

Bethany Benson (6)
Howard Primary School, Moygashel

A Pilot

He was very, very brave
He fought in World War II
His plane was very quick
Quicker than a Subaru
He was a Spitfire pilot.

Noah Stewart (6)
Howard Primary School, Moygashel

Dad

He is as funny as a clown,
He makes me laugh all the time,
Sometimes when I am bad
It makes him mad and me feel sad,
But he's the only one I will ever have,
He is my dad.

Jason Green (6)
Howard Primary School, Moygashel

A Book

I have leaves but I am not a tree.
I speak but I have no voice.
I guide but I have no finger.
I am a book.

Alexandra Boyd (6)
Howard Primary School, Moygashel

My Brother, Alex

He is as funny as a gorilla.
He is as cool as a bear.
He is as smelly as seawater.
He is as silly as a cat.
He is as ugly as a snowman.
He is as vain as a duck.
He is my brother, Alex.

Eve Phillips (6)
Hubberston (VC) Primary School, Hakin

My Mummy

She is as silly as a monkey.
She is as kind as a cat.
She is as pretty as a flower.
She is as cheeky as a monkey.
She is my mummy.

Ruby Reynolds (6)
Hubberston (VC) Primary School, Hakin

My Daddy

He is as handsome as a prince.
He is as nice as a rose.
He is as funny as a clown.
He is as cool as a pop star.
He is my daddy.

Jade Burniston (6)
Hubberston (VC) Primary School, Hakin

My Baby Sister

She is as cheeky as a dolphin
She is as sweet as a tulip.
She is as shiny as the sun.
She is as helpful as a Hoover.
She is as cool as a queen.
She is as silly as a monkey.
She is my baby sister, Kathryn.

Charlotte Shepherd (6)
Hubberston (VC) Primary School, Hakin

My Uncle, Neil

He is as cool as a rugby player
He is as fantastic as a football
He is as fast as a rocket
He is as ugly as an egg
He is my uncle, Neil.

Cameron Babb (6)
Hubberston (VC) Primary School, Hakin

Cheryl Cole

She is as sweet as a dolphin.
She is as funny as a puppy.
She is as kind as Hannah Montana.
She is as beautiful as a tulip.
She is Cheryl Cole.

Kaitlyn Carlson (6)
Hubberston (VC) Primary School, Hakin

My Friend, Nile

He is as cool as a rocket.
He is as silly as a pencil.
He is as funny as a joke.
He is as happy as a party.
He is my friend, Nile.

Charlie Kenyon (6)
Hubberston (VC) Primary School, Hakin

Cheryl Cole

She is as beautiful as a baby puppy.
She is as funny as a monkey.
She is as cool as a horse.
She is as happy as a dog.
She is as nice as a mouse.
She is as silly as a dolphin.
She is Cheryl Cole.

Lily Meddings (6)
Hubberston (VC) Primary School, Hakin

Rooney

He is as cool as my dad.
He is as funny as my nanny.
He is as silly as me.
He is as fast as a runner.
He is as rich as the prince.
He is Rooney.

Jude Picton (6)
Hubberston (VC) Primary School, Hakin

My Friend, Charlie

He is as rich as Michael Jackson
He is as cheeky as a monkey
He is as funny as an elephant
He is as happy as a cheetah
He is my friend, Charlie.

Nile Griffiths (6)
Hubberston (VC) Primary School, Hakin

My Teacher

She is as sweet as a puppy.
She is as beautiful as a rose.
She is as happy as a teacher.
She is as funny as a rabbit.
She is as red as a flower.
She is as cute as a kitten.
She is Mrs Morris, my teacher.

Lucy Burniston (6)
Hubberston (VC) Primary School, Hakin

My Nan

She is as shiny as a diamond.
She is as funny as a clown.
She is as beautiful as the Queen.
She is as sweet as a cherry.
She is as happy as Santa.
She is as nice as a puppy.
She is my nan.

Mia Adams (6)
Hubberston (VC) Primary School, Hakin

Who Am I?

I am a tall man
I am a judge
I have black hair
I always say, 'No'
My name beings with an 'S'
My last name begins with a 'C'
I have false teeth
I work on the X Factor

Who am I?

(Simon Cowell)

Robbie Dunlop (7)
Lislagan Primary School, Ballymoney

Who Am I?

I play football.
I play for a Spanish team.
I am a striker.
I sometimes play team captain.
I am number ten.
I cross in corners.
I am sometimes on the sub bench.
Who am I?

(Messi)

Daniel Dickson (7)
Lislagan Primary School, Ballymoney

Who Is He?

He is as cute as me.
He is black.
He has a tail.
He likes to go for walks.
He eats sausages.
Who is he?

(My little puppy, Cooper).

Thomas O'Donnell (7)
Lislagan Primary School, Ballymoney

Who Am I?

I have brown eyes.
I'm very fluffy.
I have a long tongue.
I'm very funny.
I have a black nose.
I have four legs.
I have cute paws.
I have little ears.
I have a long tail.
Who am I?

(My little dog, Plankton).

Laura King (7)
Lislagan Primary School, Ballymoney

Who Am I?

I have very little teeth.
I am grey.
I sometimes get trapped.
I like eating a lot.
I am very small.
I live in a hole.
I can live in the wild.
I can jump high but sometimes I can't.
Sometimes I sneak into people's houses.
People don't like me very much!
Who am I?

(A mouse).

Karli McConaghie (7)
Lislagan Primary School, Ballymoney

Who Is She?

She is like a bee.
She is as cool as a cat.
She is like the sun.
She is funky.
She is twenty-eight.
She is bigger than a mouse.
She is the best.
She has lots of wigs.
She is a good singer.
She sings 'Bad Romance'.
Who is she?

(Lady GaGa).

Abbie McLaughlin (7)
Lislagan Primary School, Ballymoney

Who Is He?

He's as funny as a clown.
He's as cheeky as a monkey.
He's got a big brain.
He's quite tall.
He likes Mohicans.
He likes hot showers.
He hates comprehension.
He's in Primary 7.
Who is he?

(Clint, my brother).

Jude Bolton (8)
Lislagan Primary School, Ballymoney

Who Am I?

I am as big as an elephant.
I like to blow water in the sea.
My name begins with the letter 'W'.
I swim in the sea.
I live in a different country than you.
Who am I?

(A whale).

Kian Hallam (7)
Lislagan Primary School, Ballymoney

Who Am I?

I am cute.
I love cuddly toys.
I have curly hair.
I love chocolate.
I like playing with hoops.
I like playing with soap.
I love playing with dolls.
I have a big brother called Ethan.
I love Hungry Hippos.
Who am I?

(Maia, my little cousin).

Rebecca Shepherd (7)
Lislagan Primary School, Ballymoney

Who Am I?

I have very sharp claws.
I live in a cage.
I have enormous teeth.
I am king of the jungle.
Who am I?

(A lion).

Adam McComb (7)
Lislagan Primary School, Ballymoney

Who Is She?

She is very pretty.
She is special.
She smells like a flower.
She shines like a light.
She wears lots of make-up.
She is a very good singer and dancer.
She wears bright colours.
She goes to East High School.
Who is she?

(Gabriella).

Georgia McIlveen (8)
Lislagan Primary School, Ballymoney

Who Am I?

I have very sharp teeth.
I can jump really high.
I live in a hot country.
I live in the wild.
I can climb trees.
I have lots of spots.
I am very fast.
Who am I?

(A cheetah).

Benny Mitchell (7)
Lislagan Primary School, Ballymoney

Who Am I?

I have black shoes.
I play football.
I play for Liverpool.
I have spiky hair.
I am good at football.
I have an 'R' in my surname.
I am thirty-two years old.
I am married.
Who am I?

(Steven Gerrard).

David Houston (8)
Lislagan Primary School, Ballymoney

Who Am I?

I live in water.
I have a long tail.
I come from Australia.
I can hurt you.
I have sharp teeth.
Who am I?

(A crocodile).

Victoria Young (7)
Lislagan Primary School, Ballymoney

Who Am I?

I am on television.
I am cute and very pretty.
I wear pretty white earrings.
I live in America.
I have an orange dress.
I have a bad brother called Bart.
I have yellow hair.
Who am I?

(Lisa Simpson).

Rebecca Hogg (7)
Lislagan Primary School, Ballymoney

Who Am I?

I am a man.
I am as cool as an ice cream.
I wear ties.
I am really funny and tell funny stories.
I wear a suit.
I am not a good dancer.
I am the boss of the school.
Who am I?

(Our headmaster, Mr Edgar).

Rhianna Elyse Todd (7)
Lislagan Primary School, Ballymoney

My Daddy

He is as famous as a rock star
He is as kind as a nurse
He is as loving as a dove
He is as funny as a clown
He is my daddy.

Kathryn Ward (6)
Pittencrieff Primary School, Dunfermline

My Dad

He is as musical as a band
He is as judgey as Simon Cowell
He is as strong as a Sumo wrestler
He is as wise as a science teacher
He is as old as the Mona Lisa
He is my dad.

David Clayton (6)
Pittencrieff Primary School, Dunfermline

My Dad

He is as clumsy as a chicken
He is as busy as a mayor
He is as strong as a gorilla
He is as clever as an owl
He is as cool as King Arthur
He is as awesome as Robert the Bruce
He is as chattery as a chatterbox
He is my dad.

Rory Neil (6)
Pittencrieff Primary School, Dunfermline

My Daddy

He is as cool as a rock star
He is as spotty as a cheetah
He is as strong as a gorilla
He is as fit as a runner
He is as busy as a worker
He is as kind as a friend
He is as bald as an egg
He is my daddy.

Oliver Price (6)
Pittencrieff Primary School, Dunfermline

My Cat, Coco

She is as black and white as a zebra.
She scratches like a tiger.
She's as funny as a monkey.
She loves cat food.
She's as nice as Ella.
She's as silly as a bee.
She loves me.
She's my cat, Coco!

Jessica Moffett (7)
Rockport School, Craigavad

Hector

He is as black as night
He is as soft as a teddy
He is hungry like a bear
He is as cuddly as my mummy
His eyes are as big as a balloon
And as brown as chocolate
I love him and he loves me
He is Hector, my Labrador.

Miles Cunningham (7)
Rockport School, Craigavad

My Kitten, Lilly

She is as cute as a puppy.
She is as loving as a dog.
She is as fierce as a tiger.
She is as playful as a monkey.
She is as funny as a clown.
She is as lazy as a pig.
She is as tabby as Jessica's toy.
She is as fast as the wind.
She is as cheeky as a chimp.
She is as sneaky as a snake.
She is as nice as Jessica.
She is as smiley as Miles.
She is as pretty as Ella.
She is as silly as a fish.
She is as lovely as Angus.
She is my kitten, Lilly.

Sacha Millar (7)
Rockport School, Craigavad

Makes Me Laugh

He has a fast car
He is stupid
He is an adult but has a teddy
He is very funny
He is Mr Bean.

Liam McIlduff (6)
Rockport School, Craigavad

My Dog, Taz

As strong as an ox
As naughty as a monkey
As cuddly as a bear
As big as a dinosaur to me
As loved as a love heart
My dog, Taz.

Alexander Hook (7)
Rockport School, Craigavad

My Cat, Monkey

He is as lazy as my dad!
He loves chicken like me.
He is as crazy as R4.
He is cheeky like a monkey.
He is as funny as a clown.
He likes chasing bugs.
He's not scared of dogs.
He likes playing with Katie.
He's the best cat in the world!
He's my cat, Monkey.

Ella Fitzpatrick (8)
Rockport School, Craigavad

Michael Jackson

He was bold
He wore a wig
He had a family
He had two sons
He had one wife
He was a pop star
And a rock star
He is dead.

He is Michael Jackson.

Kaiode Olusanya (7)
Rockport School, Craigavad

A Prehistoric Puzzle!

He was a living tank,
As big as a bus!
His club tail could kill
A tyrannosaurus!
He lived in Canada
100 million years ago,
He ate plants and bushes,
He's my favourite dino!
He is an ankylosaurus!

Ruairidh Forbes (7)
Rockport School, Craigavad

Grievous

He is black and white like a cow,
He is as fast as a raptor,
He is as smart as a dolphin,
He is a good listener like my mum,
He chews through things like my pencil sharpener,
He is my sheepdog, Grievous, that I want for my birthday.

Haydn Pick (7)
Rockport School, Craigavad

My Brother, Theo

He's as naughty as a monkey.
He's as bad as a beetle.
He's as fast as a falcon.
He's as tall as a giraffe.
He's as cool as a penguin.
He's as sneaky as a snake.
He's my brother, Theo.

Tara Rose Millar (6)
Rockport School, Craigavad

My Pet Bunnies

They are as cute as a cat
They are as funny as a clown
They are as beautiful as a flower
They are as cheeky as a monkey
And they are as naughty as me
They are my pet bunnies.

Elliana Scott Harrison (7)
Rockport School, Craigavad

My Little Sister

She is as pretty as a princess.
She is as cute as a kitten.
She is as cuddly as my teddy.
She is as cheeky as a monkey.
She is as friendly as a puppy.
She is Katie, my little sister.

Jack Calvert (7)
Rockport School, Craigavad

Leona Lewis

She is a top singer
She has the X Factor
She is in Hollywood
She has black hair
She has blue eyes
She is Leona Lewis.

Dylan Burchill (7)
Ruchill Primary School, Glasgow

Hedgehog

It has a jagged back
It curls up in a ball
It eats snails
It can camouflage itself
It is scared of people
It is a hedgehog.

Jack Dragsnes (6)
Ruchill Primary School, Glasgow

Gabriella (From HS Musical)

She sings sweetly
She loves Troy
She likes all her gang
She likes playing in her house
She is Gabriella.

Chelsea Brydon (7)
Ruchill Primary School, Glasgow

The Elephant

It is as big as a bus
It's got big feet
It has a waggy tail
It makes big footprints
It has a long waggly trunk
It likes mud baths
It has big floppy ears.

James Stafford (5)
Ruchill Primary School, Glasgow

Wayne Rooney

He is so fast.
He can score lots of goals.
He plays for Man Utd.
He is good at football.
He wears a red and white strip.
He is Wayne Rooney.

Jack McKay (7)
Ruchill Primary School, Glasgow

A Dolphin

It has got a fin.
It eats fish.
People love to swim with them.
It is very cute.
It can jump out of the water.
It is a dolphin.

Ali Kamel (7)
Ruchill Primary School, Glasgow

Sally

She can do tricks
She can walk on two paws
She can balance on one paw
She is black all over
She is my cat, Sally.

Lauren Totten (6)
Ruchill Primary School, Glasgow

My Mum Is . . .

She is as bright as the sun.
She is as cuddly as a bear.
She is as beautiful as a flower.
She is as helpful as can be.
She is always good to me.
She is my mum.

Lauren O'Boyle (7)
St Anne's Primary School, Corkey

My Daddy

He is as funny as a clown.
He is as spiky as a hedgehog.
He is as fluffy as a bear.
He loves to ride his bike with me.
He would never tell a lie.
He is always very kind.
He drives a rally car.
He is as helpful as a book.
He is as much fun as my dog.
He is my daddy.

Liam McAuley (7)
St Anne's Primary School, Corkey

Horrid Henry

He is as cheeky as a monkey.
He is as sneaky as a snake.
He is as cunning as a fox.
He is as funny as a hyena.
He is as clever as a croc.
He is as horrid as a rat.
He is Horrid Henry.

Oran Reid (6)
St Anne's Primary School, Corkey

He Is A Boy

He is as soft as a peach,
He smells just like powder,
He has two little white teeth,
He has a smile as big as the moon,
He is as funny as a clown,
He is as bald as an eagle,
He is as bright as the stars,
He is as beautiful as a flower,
He is my baby brother, Charlie.

Katie Douthart (6)
St Anne's Primary School, Corkey

My Favourite Person

She is as beautiful as a flower
She gives the best cuddles ever.
She bakes buns as good as a chef.
She sings and dances to make me smile
She is my favourite person.
She is my mummy.

Connor Dickson (6)
St Anne's Primary School, Corkey

My Daddy

He is as tall as a tree.
He is as nice as a strawberry trifle.
He makes our breakfast like a chef.
He has a farm like old McDonald.
He has a tractor like Tractor Ted.
My daddy has sheep and they have lambs.

Conall McCloskey (6)
St Anne's Primary School, Corkey

My Mum

She is as funny as a clown.
She is as beautiful as a flower.
She is as caring as a lamb.
She is as kind as a cat.
She is as good as a bird.
She is as wonderful as a tree.
She is my mum.

Ella Sullivan (7)
St Anne's Primary School, Corkey

My Mum

She is kind
She is beautiful
She makes me laugh
She buys me toys
She reads me stories
She gives me lots of hugs and kisses
She is my mum.

Bernadine Hegarty (7)
St Anne's Primary School, Corkey

Maxwell

He is as strong as a gorilla.
He is as loveable as my mum.
He is as awesome as me.
He is as fast as an ostrich.
He is as generous as me.
He is as funny as a circus.
He is as excited as Kai.
He is as much fun as Owen.
He is as good as a gorilla.
He is as big as the Eiffel Tower.
He is as good as TJ.
He is as happy as my dad.
He is as kind as Kai.
He is my dog, Maxwell.

Mark Johnston (7)
St Anthony's Primary School, Larne

I Love My Mum

She is as cuddly as a bunny.
She is as happy as a smiley face.
She is as fabulous as Cheryl Cole.
She is as tall as a tree.
She is as fashionable as Hello Kitty.
She is as important as my sister.
She is as pretty as me.
She is as cool as the sun.
She is as soft as a teddy.
She is Mum.

Cara Lemon (7)
St Anthony's Primary School, Larne

Fernando Torres

He's as fast as a car.
He's as big as a gorilla.
He's as good as a game.
He's as brilliant as a football.
He's as cool as an ice cube.
He's as tall as a giraffe.
He's Fernando Torres.

Luke Magee (7)
St Anthony's Primary School, Larne

Amy

She is as funny as a clown.
She is as friendly as Sam.
She is as sweet as sweets.
She is as pretty as me.
She is as kind as Holly.
She is as happy as Larry.
She is as fashionable as Megan.
She is as cuddly as a teddy.
She is as soft as a cushion.
She is as tall as TJ.
She is my friend, Amy.

Kallie Joanne McKeown (7)
St Anthony's Primary School, Larne

My Favourite Singer, Miley Cyrus

She is as funny as a clown.
She is as pretty as a bunny.
She is as southern as a Southerner.
She is as funky as a rocker.
She is as sweet as a pear drop.
She is as happy as a puppy.
She is as good a singer as the boys in Westlife.
She is Miley Cyrus.

Niamh Walsh (7)
St Anthony's Primary School, Larne

Maxwell And You

He is as good as Santa.
He is as soft as hair.
He is as hyper as a jumping kangaroo.
He is as funny as a clown.
He is as fast as a cheetah.
He is as awesome as you.
He is my dog, Maxwell.

Owen Johnston (7)
St Anthony's Primary School, Larne

I Love My Teacher

She is as happy as a jumping jack.
She is as fashionable as a model.
She is as cool as a rock chick.
She is as small as a caterpillar.
She is as lovely as a heart.
She is as kind as Santa.
She is as pretty as a flower.
She is my teacher.

Anna Ewings (7)
St Anthony's Primary School, Larne

Tristan's First Poem

He was as friendly as my friend, Archie
He danced as cool as a leopard
He was as happy as my mummy
He sang as great as a choir
He was Michael Jackson.

Tristan Ho (6)
Sciennes Primary School, Edinburgh

Untitled

He is a karate cat
He is as fat as a lion
He is a sneaky cat
He is as soft as a teddy
He is Tinkerbell, my cat.

Ben Smyth (6)
Sciennes Primary School, Edinburgh

Untitled

He is as funny as a hyena
He is as loud as a crow
He is as smiley as a monkey
He is as cool as a cucumber
He is as tall as a wall
He is Stephen, my friend.

Matthew Caldwell (7)
Sciennes Primary School, Edinburgh

Untitled

He is as small as a mouse
He is as loud as a gorilla
He is as smiley as a happy bear
He is as friendly as a cat
He is as fast as a cheetah
He is as chatty as a parrot
He is Matthew, my friend.

Stephen Tiplady (6)
Sciennes Primary School, Edinburgh

Untitled

He is as cuddly as a cushion
He is as soft as a cat
He is as quiet as a mouse
He is as furry as a log
He is as nibbly as a mouse
He is Furry, my hamster.

Susannah Kernohan (6)
Sciennes Primary School, Edinburgh

Untitled

He is as loud as a tiger
He is as fierce as a snake
He is as naughty as a monkey
He is as big as an elephant
He is as friendly as a cat
He is as fast as a cheetah
He is a lion.

Rose Newman (6)
Sciennes Primary School, Edinburgh

Untitled

He is as athletic as an acrobat
He is as white as a cloud
He is as brave as a crocodile
He is as strong as an elephant
He is Luke Skywalker
He is my hero.

Matthew Ross (6)
Sciennes Primary School, Edinburgh

My Friend

He is as friendly as Santa
He is as black as night
He is as cuddly as a toy
He is as old as hills
He is Pepe, my cat.

Jonathan Fox (6)
Sciennes Primary School, Edinburgh

Untitled

He is as spotty as a snowman
He is furry
He is happy
He is a leopard
He is Tiger
He is my leopard.

Liza Gogoliuk (6)
Sciennes Primary School, Edinburgh

Untitled

Tiger tiger has a striped body
Opposite to the zebra but with stripes on his face
It can almost climb up trees
They grow very tall
They are very vicious
They have very sharp claws.

Hamish Croft (6)
Sciennes Primary School, Edinburgh

She Is

She is as cheeky as a monkey
She is as silly as a hyena
She is as cute as a baby tiger
She's as naughty as my cousin Stanley
She is as happy as me
She is as nosy as my sister
She is my dog.

Molly Maccoll-Baker (6)
Sciennes Primary School, Edinburgh

Who Is He?

He is as quiet as a mouse
He is as shy as a squirrel
He is as kind as a buddy
He is as brave as a superhero
He is as strong as a wrestler
He is Ralph.

Freya Clarkson (6)
Sciennes Primary School, Edinburgh

Tiffany

She is as funny as a clown
She is as loud as an elephant
She is as naughty as a pirate
She is as brave as a cat
She is as cute as a teddy bear
She is as happy as me
She is my Tiff, my cat.

Grace Marshall (7)
Sciennes Primary School, Edinburgh

Untitled

He is as helpful as my dad
He is as bossy as a boot
He is as cool as a parrot
He is as tall as a flamingo
He is as kind as my mum
He is as fit as Ronaldo
He is as bashed as a stone
He is John Wayne, my hero.

Dante Gargaro (7)
Sciennes Primary School, Edinburgh

Sasha

She is as funny as a cat
She is as cute as a cat
She is as cheeky as can be
She is as furry as a cat
She is sometimes silly
She is my dog, Sashakins.

Mhairi Morrison (7)
Sciennes Primary School, Edinburgh

Untitled

He is as soft as a cloud
He is as swift as a cheetah
He is as possessive as the orange skin is over the segments
He is as creeping as night is when it falls
He is as silent as the autumn leaves
He is as proud as the Queen
He is as strong as a bear
He is as golden as a star
He is a lion, my favourite animal.

Brianna Baxter Stevenson (7)
Sciennes Primary School, Edinburgh

My First Riddle

He is as funny as Tom and Jerry,
He is as colourful as a parrot,
He is as crazy as a monkey,
He is as jumpy as a kangaroo,
He is as stupid as a coconut,
He is as wild as a cheetah.
He is a clown.

Rory Bruno Williamson (6)
Sinclairtown Primary School, Kirkcaldy

My First Riddle

She is as cool as ice cream
She is as beautiful as a flower,
She is as funny as a clown,
She is as loud as a monkey,
She is as famous as a stage,
She is Hannah Montana.

Samantha Fenton (6)
Sinclairtown Primary School, Kirkcaldy

My First Riddle

He is as helpful as a policeman,
He is as wild as a clown,
He is as lazy as a cloud,
He is as cool as an ice cream,
He is as cute as a baby.
He is my daddy.

Eildhi Forrest (6)
Sinclairtown Primary School, Kirkcaldy

My First Riddle

She is as brave as a lioness,
She is as pretty as a princess,
She is as funny as a joke,
She is as tidy as a hamster,
She is as clever as a professor.
She is my best friend, Amelia.

Darcey McDade (6)
Sinclairtown Primary School, Kirkcaldy

My First Riddle

He is as funny as a clown,
He is as noisy as a dog,
He has a nose as long as a giraffe,
He is as yellow as the sun,
He is as spongy as a sponge,
He is as silly as a dog.
He is SpongeBob.

Lucy Armit (6)
Sinclairtown Primary School, Kirkcaldy

My First Riddle

She is as beautiful as a cat,
She is as funny as a clown,
She is as famous as a rich man,
She is as tall as a bear,
She can sing like a bird.
She is Hannah Montana.

Emily Ferguson (5)
Sinclairtown Primary School, Kirkcaldy

My First Riddle

He is as funny as a joke,
He is as cool as a rock star,
He is as old as a dinosaur,
He is as fast as a cheetah,
He is as kind as me.
He is my grandad.

Logan McGinley (6)
Sinclairtown Primary School, Kirkcaldy

My First Riddle

He is as muscly as Mr Muscle,
He is as wonderful as a rainbow,
He is as rescuing as a fireman,
He is as funny as a clown,
He is as crazy as a person.
He is Spider-Man.

Demi-Lee Wilson (6)
Sinclairtown Primary School, Kirkcaldy

My First Riddle

She is as kind as a teacher,
She is as small as a mouse,
She is as funny as a clown,
She is as friendly as a puppy.
She is my friend, Cerys.

Niamh Bushnell (5)
Sinclairtown Primary School, Kirkcaldy

My First Riddle

She is as funny as a hedgehog,
She is as bad as a parrot,
She is as loud as a monkey,
She is as helpful as a dinner lady,
She is as beautiful as me,
She is as blonde as a butterfly.
She is my mum.

Daniella Tait (6)
Sinclairtown Primary School, Kirkcaldy

My First Riddle

She is as cute as a baby,
She is as jumpy as a monkey,
She is as cuddly as a teddy bear,
She is as crazy as lightning,
She is as funny as a clown.
She is my cat, Lotta.

Ethan Whyley (6)
Sinclairtown Primary School, Kirkcaldy

My First Riddle

He is as strong as an elephant,
He is as big as a giraffe,
He is as bad as a crocodile,
He is as silver as a 10p.
He is Megatron, my Transformer.

Murray Evans (5)
Sinclairtown Primary School, Kirkcaldy

My First Riddle

She is as cuddly as a teddy bear,
She is as nice as a flower,
She is as beautiful as a rainbow,
She is as helpful as a doctor.
She is my mummy.

Jessica Smillie (5)
Sinclairtown Primary School, Kirkcaldy

My First Riddle

He is as helpful as the teacher,
He is as cute as a puppy,
He is as yellow as a banana,
He is as good as my friend.
He is Bumble Bee, my Transformer.

Scott Kilpatrick (6)
Sinclairtown Primary School, Kirkcaldy

Aaron

He's as funny as a clown,
He's as multicoloured as a check board,
He's as furry as a monkey,
He's as tall as a Mini car boot,
He's as silly as my dog.
He's an alien.

Max Davie (8)
Sinclairtown Primary School, Kirkcaldy

My Riddle

She's as cute as a pony
She's as clean as white clothes
She's as puffy as a puffy teddy bear
She's as white as snow
She's as small as a dog
She's as smart as a teacher
She's as fast as a cheetah
She is Cassie the cat.

Tara Martin (7)
Sinclairtown Primary School, Kirkcaldy

My Barry

He's as big as a car
He's as scary as a ghost
He's as orange as an orange
He's as stripy as a zebra
His teeth are as pointy as a dragon's
He's a tiger.

Sam Emmerson (7)
Sinclairtown Primary School, Kirkcaldy

My Pet Evil

He's as scary as a lion
He's as strong as lava
He's as sneaky as a flying bird
He's as big as a tree
He's as black as the ground
He's as mean as a lion
He's a dragon.

Declan Toshack (8)
Sinclairtown Primary School, Kirkcaldy

My Pet Max

He's as fast as a butterfly,
He's as hairy as a pig,
He's as skinny as a box,
He's as funny as a clown,
He's as wild as a bull,
He's as dirty as a farmer,
He's as messy as a dog,
He's as jumpy as a kid,
He's as quiet as a mouse,
He's as nice as a flower,
He's as smart as a banana.

Rebecca Brown (8)
Sinclairtown Primary School, Kirkcaldy

Liz The Elephant

She's as big as a giraffe,
She's as loud as thunder,
She's as cheeky as a monkey,
She's as funny as a clown,
She's as nervous as an actor,
She's as happy as the sun,
She's as cute as a kitten,
She's as grey as a raincloud,
She's as bubbly as a fairy,
She's as active as a runner, well almost!
She's as heavy as a house,
She's as jolly as an entertainer,
She's as wet as a fish.
She's an elephant!

Erin Brown (8)
Sinclairtown Primary School, Kirkcaldy

My Pet Spike

He's as small as a pencil,
He's as long as a log,
He's as skinny as a pot,
He's as green as a glass bottle,
He's as spiky as a knife,
He's as cool as a cool dude,
He's as rough as sandpaper,
He's as sneaky as a fly.
He's my bearded dragon.

Jonathan Balfour (8)
Sinclairtown Primary School, Kirkcaldy

My Pet Missty

She's as noisy as a miaow,
She's as naughty as a bad dog,
She's as fast as Logan in a house run,
She's as silly as Lee,
She's as stupid as me.
She's my kitten, Missty.

Scott Pearson (8)
Sinclairtown Primary School, Kirkcaldy

Eric The Elephant Riddle

He's a noisy as an earthquake
He's as tall as a giraffe
He's as grey as dark clouds
He's as slow as a snail
He's as cool as me
He's as sporty as my dad
He's as cheeky as anything
He's Eric the elephant.

Ryan Hunter (8)
Sinclairtown Primary School, Kirkcaldy

Pilchard The Cat

He's as stripy as a tiger
He's as grey as a cloud
He's as black as mud
He's as tall as a ruler
He's as long as a box
He's as cute as a mouse
He's as soft as a carpet
He's my pet cat.

Myles Mark Bolton (8)
Sinclairtown Primary School, Kirkcaldy

The Scary Man

He's as scary as thunder
He's as fast as a cheetah
He's as scary as a spider
He's as smooth as a cat
He growls like a dog,
He's as long as a plane,
He's as cheeky as a cheetah
He's a tiger.

Connor James Elder (8)
Sinclairtown Primary School, Kirkcaldy

My Pet Evil

He's as strong as God,
He's as bad as a devil,
He's as big as a dark elephant,
He's as scary as an alien,
He's as sneaky as a dark droid,
He's as brave as a pharaoh,
He's as quiet as the wind,
He's as dark as a dark lion.
He's my pet evil dragon.

Ginters Kubulnieks (8)
Sinclairtown Primary School, Kirkcaldy

My Pet Liz

She's as cute as a love heart,
She's as small as a mouse,
She's as green as the leaves,
She's as slim as a pencil,
She's as quick as the water from the tap,
She's as smooth as a snake,
She's as long as a book,
She's as young as a baby human,
She's as camouflaged as a cheetah.
She's my pet, Liz the lizard.

Kate Matheson (7)
Sinclairtown Primary School, Kirkcaldy

My Pet

He's as tall as I am
He's as small as a lion
He's as cheeky as me
He's as funny as Logan
He's as brown as a bear
He's my monkey.

Jordan Thomson (7)
Sinclairtown Primary School, Kirkcaldy

My Animal

She's as tall as a chair
She's as cute as a button
She's as furry as my bed cover
She's as warm as a bath
She's as fast as a tiger
She's as playful as a toy
She's as quiet as a mouse
She's as sleepy as me on a Monday morning.
She is my pet dog.

Justine McIvor (8)
Sinclairtown Primary School, Kirkcaldy

My Pet Donkey

He's as grey as a raincloud,
He's as fast as a horse,
He's as big as a car,
He's as fun as my sister,
He's as cheeky as my brother,
He's as quiet as a mouse,
He's as sneaky as a tiger.
He's my pet donkey.

Molly Burns (7)
Sinclairtown Primary School, Kirkcaldy

My Cheetah

He's as long as a table,
He's as fast as a lion,
He's as yellow and spotty as a giraffe,
He's as tall as a window,
He's as big as a dragon,
He's as fluffy as a bear,
He's as talented as a monkey.
It is a cheetah.

Logan McLeod (8)
Sinclairtown Primary School, Kirkcaldy

My Pet

He's as grey as an elephant,
He's as long as a one metre stick,
He's as tall as two bookshelves,
His eyes are as blue as the sea,
He sounds like a horse,
He's as soft as a mouse,
He smells like a farm.
He's a donkey.

Kirstin Brown (8)
Sinclairtown Primary School, Kirkcaldy

Slowmotion The Crocodile

He's as scary as a dinosaur,
He's as colourful as a rainbow,
He's as loud as a storm,
He's as long as a box,
He's as big as 1m 59cm,
He's as magical as Harry Potter,
He's as fluffy as a bean bag,
He's as funny as my dad,
He's as bored as my sisters,
He's as slow as a tortoise,
He's as sad as my grandad,
He's as sharp as dinosaurs' teeth.
He is Slowmotion the crocodile.

Lewis Smillie (8)
Sinclairtown Primary School, Kirkcaldy

Dan The Snake

He's as long as a sausage dog,
He's as scaly as a crocodile,
He's as tall as a rubber,
He's as fast as lightning,
He's as dangerous as a dinosaur,
He's as brown as mud,
He's as deadly as poison,
He's as sneaky as a ninja.
He is Dan the snake.

Daniel Easson (8)
Sinclairtown Primary School, Kirkcaldy

My Pet Elephant

She's as glittery as a snowball,
She's as greedy as a monkey,
She's as fat as the school,
She's as quiet as a teddy bear,
She's as cute as a horse,
She's as good as a monkey,
She's as strong as a dinosaur,
She's my pet elephant.

Ally Carr (7)
Sinclairtown Primary School, Kirkcaldy

My Mum

She is as sleepy as a lazy rat
She is as kind as a fairy
She is as funny as a clown
She is as nice as a friend
She is as gentle as the dentist
She is as caring as a nurse
She dresses like a model
She is my mum.

Eve Wywalec (8)
Sinclairtown Primary School, Kirkcaldy

Lumpy

It is as purple as a violet sky,
It is as great as my mum and dad,
It is beautiful like a puppy dog,
It is as small as a baby elephant,
It is as cuddly as a pillow,
It is as cute as a baby,
It is as funny as a clown,
It is as kind as a cat.
It is my teddy, Lumpy!

Alix Brown (9)
Sinclairtown Primary School, Kirkcaldy

My Big Cousin, Heather

She is as popular as Beyoncé
She has blue eyes as big as the sky
She is as cute as a newborn puppy
She is as funny as a hyena
She is as fast as a cheetah
She is as silly as a monkey
She is as chatty as a parrot
She is as talented as Joe McElderry,
She has blonde hair as bright as the sun.
She is my big cousin, Heather.

Jolie McDade (9)
Sinclairtown Primary School, Kirkcaldy

My Auntie

She is as funny as a clown
She is as talented as the X Factor contestant
She is as fit as a fiddle
She is as pretty as Cheryl Cole
She is as helpful as a teacher
She is as good a cook as the Masterchef
She is as strong as a boxer
She is my auntie, Lynne.

Samantha McGlashan (8)
Sinclairtown Primary School, Kirkcaldy

Sara

She is as clever as me
She is as cool as a kangaroo
She is as cheery as Santa Claus
She is as funny as a comedian
She is as beautiful as a flower
She is as helpful as a maid
She is as joyful as a dog
She is as amazing as a star
She is as responsible as a teacher
She is as healthy as an apple
She is my cousin, Sara.

Rosa Williamson (9)
Sinclairtown Primary School, Kirkcaldy

Splash Flipper

It is as flexible as a gymnast,
It is as cute as a kitten,
It is as caring as a nurse,
It is as cuddly as a teddy bear,
It is as shiny as a clear window,
It is as kind as my mum,
It splashes like a whale,
It is as beautiful as a butterfly.
It is a dolphin.

Amy Bushnell (9)
Sinclairtown Primary School, Kirkcaldy

Gregory Tade

He is as fast as a tiger
He is as big as my dad
He is as fit as a cheetah
He is as talented as Steven Gerrard
He is as friendly as a puppy
He is as kind as my mum
He is a footballer like Fernando Torres
He is built like a boxer
He is Gregory Tade.

Harris Hutchison (9)
Sinclairtown Primary School, Kirkcaldy

White Tiger

It is as strong as a great white shark,
It is as rare as a jaguar,
It is as stripy as a zebra,
It is as fierce as a black bear,
It is as dangerous as a king cobra,
It has blue eyes like the sky,
It is as fast as a cheetah,
It is as cool as Rangers,
It can swim as good as me,
It kills like a lion.
That's a white tiger for you!

Gregor Skinner (9)
Sinclairtown Primary School, Kirkcaldy

SpongeBob SquarePants

He is as funny as a bunny
He is as small as a baby hippo
He is as spongy as a fairy cake
He is as cuddly as a teddy bear
He is as flexible as a gymnast
He has got one friend who's called Patrick
He has got holes in his body like cheese
He is SpongeBob SquarePants!

Emmalisa Peggie (9)
Sinclairtown Primary School, Kirkcaldy

My Dad

He is as cool as a DJ
He is as sporty as a runner
He is as funny as a comedian
He is fun like a clown
He is as well as a doctor
He is as strong as a wrestler
He is as helpful as a waiter
He is as kind as my best friend
He is my dad.

Joshua Paul McCormack (10)
Sinclairtown Primary School, Kirkcaldy

Floss

She is as fast as a lion
She is as caring as a nurse
She can kick a ball as good as Torres
She is as good at jumping as a kangaroo
She is as smart as a computer
She is as fit as a fiddle
She is as soft and as cuddly as a teddy
She is as fierce as a bear
She is as swift as a cheetah
She is my best friend, Floss.

Matthew Adam (10)
Sinclairtown Primary School, Kirkcaldy

Infernape

It's as fierce as a dinosaur
It's as fast as a cheetah
Its breath is worse than a dragon's
It's as brave as an eagle
It's as cheeky as a monkey
It can jump higher than a hurdler
It is my favourite Pokémon, Infernape.

Scott Thomson (10)
Sinclairtown Primary School, Kirkcaldy

My Dog

She is as fun as a jack-in-the-box
She is as fat as a hare
She is as fluffy as a teddy bear
She is as cute as a fluffy ball
She is my dog.

Morgan McDougall (9)
Sinclairtown Primary School, Kirkcaldy

Mudkip (Pokémon)

It is as cute as a pup
It is as funny as a clown
It is as cool as a lion
It loves water like a fish
It is nice like a cat
It is playful like a dog
It is cuddly like a teddy
It is Mudkip.

James McCallum (9)
Sinclairtown Primary School, Kirkcaldy

Jason Derulo

He is as cool as a cucumber
He sings as good as Usher
He is as smart as the Black Eyed Peas
He is as funny as a clown
He is as rich as Simon Cowell
He dances like a pop star
He is Jason Derulo.

Blair McPhee (10)
Sinclairtown Primary School, Kirkcaldy

Mewtwo

He is as happy as a monkey
He is as old as my dad
He is as kind as my mum
He is as smart as a teacher
He is as clever as three people
He is as good as me
He is as kind as a pet
He is a Pokémon called Mewtwo.

Lewis Ross (10)
Sinclairtown Primary School, Kirkcaldy

Bart Simpson

He is funny like a clown
He likes to skateboard
He is yellow like the sun
He's from Springfield
He's naughty like a school boy
He's an American boy
He's got spiky hair like a hedgehog
He is Bart Simpson.

Cameron Ross (10)
Sinclairtown Primary School, Kirkcaldy

Cat

It's as small as my toys.
It's black and white like a zebra crossing.
It's as cuddly as a teddy.
It's a cat.

Cameron Kane (6)
Thornliebank Primary School, Thornliebank

Puppy

It's as small as a daisy.
It's as brown as a tree.
It's as wonderful as chocolate.
It's a puppy.

Abbie Kennedy (6)
Thornliebank Primary School, Thornliebank

Monkey

It's as big as my sister.
It's as brown as a tree.
It's as fast as a roadrunner.
It's a monkey.

Natalie O'Mara (6)
Thornliebank Primary School, Thornliebank

Parrot

It's as small as a toy.
It's as colourful as a rainbow.
It's as lovely as a cat.
It's a parrot.

Lawizah Shahbaz (6)
Thornliebank Primary School, Thornliebank

Young Writers Information

We hope you have enjoyed reading this book - and that you will continue to enjoy it in the coming years.
If you like reading and writing poetry drop us a line, or give us a call, and we'll send you a free information pack.
Alternatively if you would like to order further copies of this book or any of our other titles, then please give us a call or log onto our website at www.youngwriters.co.uk.

Young Writers Information
Remus House
Coltsfoot Drive
Peterborough
PE2 9BF
(01733) 890066